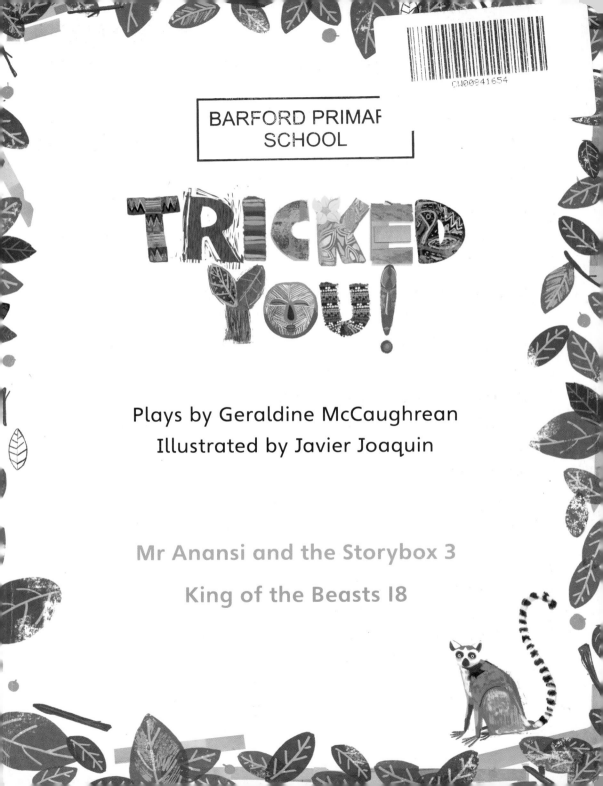

TRICKED YOU!

Plays by Geraldine McCaughrean

Illustrated by Javier Joaquin

Published by Pearson Education Limited, Edinburgh Gate, Harlow, Essex, CM20 2JE.

www.pearsonschools.co.uk

Text © Geraldine McCaughrean 2013

Designed by Georgia Styring
Original illustrations © Javier Joaquin 2013
Illustrated by Javier Joaquin, The Organisation
Cover design by Javier Joaquin

The right of Geraldine McCaughrean to be identified as author of this work has been
asserted by her in accordance with the Copyright, Designs and Patents Act 1988.

First published 2013

17 16 15 14 13
10 9 8 7 6 5 4 3 2 1

British Library Cataloguing in Publication Data
A catalogue record for this book is available from the British Library

ISBN 978 0 435 14419 7

Printed and bound in the UK by Ashford Colour Press.

Acknowledgements
We would like to thank Bangor Central Integrated Primary School, Northern Ireland;
Bishop Henderson Church of England Primary School, Somerset; Bletchingdon Parochial
Church of England Primary School, Oxfordshire; Brookside Community Primary School,
Somerset; Bude Park Primary School, Hull; Carisbrooke Church of England Primary School,
Isle of Wight; Cheddington Combined School, Buckinghamshire; Dair House Independent
School, Buckinghamshire; Deal Parochial School, Kent; Glebe Infant School, Goucestershire;
Henley Green Primary School, Coventry; Lovelace Primary School, Surrey; Our Lady of Peace
Junior School, Slough; Tackley Church of England Primary School, Oxfordshire; and Twyford
Church of England School, Buckinghamshire for their invaluable help in the development
and trialling of the Bug Club resources.

Every effort has been made to contact copyright holders of material reproduced in this
book. Any omissions will be rectified in subsequent printings if notice is given to the
publishers.

Mr Anansi and the Storybox

Characters

Mr Anansi

Maker Bossman – a god

Nelly – the Anansis' neighbour

Mrs Anansi

Tolly – the Anansis' neighbour

Rainbow Python
Leopard
Hornets
– played by the
same person

Nelly: What's your husband doing, Mrs Anansi, climbing that tree?

Tolly: He's up to **some** mischief.

Nelly: Getting above himself, I bet.

Mrs Anansi: My Mr Anansi's going up in the world, that's what. He's gone to visit Maker Bossman.

At the top of the tree, Maker Bossman is holding a box.

Mr Anansi: That's one fine box, Maker Bossman.

Maker:	Push off, Mr Anansi. You're trespassing.
Mr Anansi:	Is that your box, Maker?
Maker:	It is my own personal box of tales.
Mr Anansi:	Tails? What, like tiger's tails? Snail's tails?
Maker:	Snails don't have ... Look, this is **my** box of stories, right?
Mr Anansi:	Stories? What are stories? I wish **I** had a box like that.
Maker:	There **is** no other box like this. All the stories in the world are in here. And they're all mine.
Mr Anansi:	Didn't your mother teach you to share?
Maker:	Cheeky rascal! I don't have a mother. I made everything myself – including myself. Now go away.

Mr Anansi: How much would I need to buy that box?

Maker: Did I say there was a price?

Mr Anansi: Everything has a price.

Maker: Very well, then. The price is ...
the spots off a leopard, the colours of
the rainbow and a fistful of hornets.
Then, if you can tell me what I'm
thinking, the box is yours.

Mr Anansi: I'm on it, man!

Mr Anansi comes down the tree.

Nelly: Well, Mr Anansi?

Tolly: What did Maker say?

Mrs Anansi: You're looking rattled, husband.

Mr Anansi: I'm thriving, wife. Nothing rattles Mr Anansi man. Er ... I need to fetch some things for Maker Bossman. How am I going to get Leopard's spots? D'you think he takes off his fur at night?

Mrs Anansi: A-ha! What **you** need is a deep hole.

Mr Anansi: I see what you mean!

Nelly: I wish I did.

Tolly: Look, here comes Leopard! Watch out, Mr Anansi!

Mrs Anansi: I'd better start digging.

Nelly: You're **gardening** when your husband's going to get eaten?

Leopard enters.

Mr Anansi: Hey, Leopard. Congratulations!

Leopard: Grrrr! ... Er ... why?

Mr Anansi: You won the talent contest.
Maker Bossman-Up-Top says you're
the finest dancer in the jungle!

Leopard: "Finest dancer in the jungle", eh?

Mr Anansi: Maker says you're so good at dancing,
you can do it with your eyes closed!
Is that true?

Leopard: Why? Are you saying it's not? Grrrrr!

Mr Anansi: Not at all! I'd just love to see it. Dancing
with your eyes shut? Wow!

Leopard: Just watch me!

Leopard dances into the pit Mrs Anansi has dug.
The fall makes his spots fall off.

Mrs Anansi: Oh, you poor thing, Leopard! Let me help you out.

Nelly: Look at that! A leopard with no spots.

Mrs Anansi: He landed so hard, they all dropped off.

Leopard exits, embarrassed.

Maker: Clever as ever. But Mr Anansi won't get a rainbow, not in a month of mangoes.

Mrs Anansi: What do you need next, husband?

Mr Anansi: The colours of the rainbow. Hmm ...

Mrs Anansi: What **you** need is a rainbow python, a tree and some string.

Tolly: A snake? A tree and some string?

Mr Anansi: I get your drift!

Nelly: I don't.

Mrs Anansi cuts down a tree.

Tolly: Look, here comes Rainbow Python!

Python enters. Mr Anansi picks up the tree.

Nelly: Mrs Anansi! Rainbow Python's going to swallow your husband! I can't look!

Mr Anansi is talking to the tree.

Mr Anansi: Yes, I know you'd like to think so, but you're wrong ...

Python: To whom are you sssspeaking, foolisssshh Misssster Anansssi?

Mr Anansi: To Tree here. **Tree** says it's taller than anyone, but I say that you're longer, Rainbow Python.

Python: Of course I'm longer. Everyone knowsss it.

Mr Anansi: Well, let's see. Lie down next to Tree, and I'll compare you.

Python: Sssseee? I'm longer. No contessssst.

Mr Anansi: Hmmm. It's close. May I straighten out your kinks, Python?

Python: Unkink me! I'm longessst. Ooo, that ticklessss!

Mr Anansi: Now I'll just tie you to the tree ... And there's my rainbow! That only leaves the hornets.

Maker: Clever as ever, Mr Anansi, but you won't catch hornets ... or, if you do, you'll wish you hadn't.

Python: Hey! Untie me, will you? Oi!

Mr Anansi: Hornets. Hornets. Hmm ...

Mrs Anansi: What **you** need is a coconut, a banana leaf and a cup of water.

Mr Anansi: I see where you're coming from!

Nelly: A coconut?

Tolly: A banana leaf?

Nelly: A cup of ... LOOK OUT! HORNETS!

Mr Anansi puts the banana leaf on his head, holds up the coconut halves and Mrs Anansi tips the water over him.

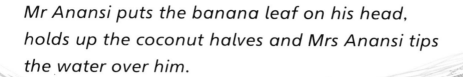

Hornets: Bzzzzzz!

Mr Anansi: Hey, take cover, hornet brothers! The monsoon's going to splatter you and break your lovely wings!

Maker: The monsoon? Already? I don't remember starting the monsoon ...

Mrs Anansi: Why else would a man be standing drip-dripping, with a banana leaf on his head?

Mr Anansi: Here! Quick, Hornets! Shelter in these coconut shells!

Buzzing suddenly stops. Mr Anansi closes the two halves of the coconut.

Mr Anansi climbs the tree.

Mr Anansi: Well, Maker, here are your three gifts.

Maker: Clever as ever, Mr Anansi. But you'll never guess what I'm ...

Mr Anansi: What you're thinking? You're thinking, "If that villain Mr Anansi thinks he can trick me out of my box, he can think again."

Maker sulks.

Maker: Clever as ever. Here you are, then.

Maker hands over the box.

Nelly: What's in the box, Mr Anansi?

Tolly: If it's treasure, he'll surely keep it to himself!

Mrs Anansi: Empty out the box, husband!

Mr Anansi: LOOK OUT BELOW!

He empties the box and the stories fall out.

Maker: You go to all that trouble, and then set them loose?!

Mr Anansi: What's mine to have is mine to let go.

Tolly: Adventure stories! Magic stories! Ohhh!

Nelly: Romances! Myths! Ahhh!

Mrs Anansi: Legends, mysteries!

Maker: You're forgetting something, Mr Anansi. I've got a fistful of hornets here! Watch out ...

Mrs Anansi: Listen up, neighbours. Are you going to let Bossman Maker-Up-Top hurt Storyman Anansi?

Nelly: Never! We'll hide you, man!

Tolly: You can stay at my place!

Nelly: You're our hero, Mr Anansi!

Mr Anansi, Mrs Anansi, Nelly and Tolly exit.
Maker frees the hornets.

Hornets: Bzzzzz ...

Maker: After him, Hornets! OH NO! Too late – they're going for me! Ow! Not me, silly! Mr Anansi, not me! Ouch! Do you know who I am? OW! I forbid you ... ooch! To sting me ... ouch! Stop it! Aaaaaah!

Hornets chase Maker offstage.

King of the Beasts

Characters

Mole	Wolf
Lark	Elephant
Giraffe	Hippo

Lark is lying on the ground. Mole enters and almost steps on her.

Lark: Oh, please! Don't tread on me!

Mole: Oh my soul! I'm as blind as a mole!

Lark: You **are** a mole.

Mole: That's true. Did I hurt you?

Lark: Not you. I was in a mid-air collision with a duck.

Mole: Well, you can't lie here! The competitors will trample you flat. Here, let me help you out of the way. Have a drink of this water.

Lark: What a friend you are! I feel much better now. What were you saying about competitors? Is there going to be a race?

Mole: Don't you know? This is Election Day, when everyone competes to be King or Queen of the Animals for a year and a day.

Lark:	Good gracious. Have you ever won?

Mole laughs.

Mole:	Me? It's always Elephant.

Offstage, Elephant trumpets.

Elephant:	Harrooo!
Lark:	Elephant **always** wins?
Mole:	Of course. He's big. And he can catch.
Lark:	What's catching got to do with it? And big isn't always best. Look at the Big Bad Wolf.

Wolf, Hippo and Giraffe enter.

Wolf: Is someone talking about me?

Mole: Oh, hello, Wolf. Hello, Hippo and Giraffe! This is Lark.

Wolf: Nice to eat ... I mean, **meet** you.

Hippo: What are **you** doing here, Mole? There's no way **you** could win! You can't see well enough to catch a cold.

Mole: Have you forgotten, Hippo? We all have to enter the competition – all of us four-legged animals. You're lucky you're a bird, Lark!

Lark: Who says you have to enter?

Giraffe: Elephant, of course.

Hippo: He's the king.

Giraffe: But maybe not for long. This year I'm taller. This could be my year!

Wolf: But you can't catch, butter-mouth.

Giraffe: I've been practising.

Lark: What are you supposed to be catching?

Hippo: You'll see.

Mole: But everyone knows it's always ...

Offstage, Elephant trumpets.

Elephant: Harrooo! Harrooo!

Lark: What **is** that terrible noise?

Giraffe: That's Elephant blowing his own trumpet.

Hippo: Of course. It's always Elephant.

Wolf: Here come the other animals.

Mole: Hello, Lion! Morning, Zebra! How are you, Mr Gnu?

Giraffe: Hey, Hartebeest. See how tall I've grown?

Enter Elephant.

Elephant: Kneel down! Anyone with knees, kneel down! **We** have arrived.

The others greet him unenthusiastically.

All:  Hail, King Elephant.

Elephant: Welcome, subjects. Happy Election Day. In the past, We have always thrown a lemon in the air, and whoever caught it became King. This year the rules have changed.
(A gasp of raised hopes from the other animals.)
This year it will be a gooseberry!
(A sigh of dashed hopes.)

Wolf: And he will reach up and catch it in his trunk.

Hippo: It's like a baseball mitt, that trunk.

Wolf: He reaches, he sucks in the fruit ...

Giraffe: ... and he wins.

Mole: How are you feeling now, Lark?

Lark: Much better, thank you. But you're trembling, Mole. Are you scared? Cheer up – you might win!

Mole: No, I shall just get stood on. I never even **see** the fruit: my eyesight's terrible.

Hippo: Scaredy Mole!

Elephant: Everyone ready? We will throw the gooseberry after three.

All: One, two, three ... GO!

All but Mole and Lark run to and fro in slow motion.
Lark flutters.

Lark: Up it flies, higher than high. But I can fly high, too!

Giraffe: Me – me – me – me! Out of my way.

Elephant: Those with knees: prepare to need them!

A pause.

Hippo: So ... Is it Elephant again?

Elephant: Where is the gooseberry?
Is it in Our trunk?

Wolf: Well, I haven't got it.

Hippo: Nor me.

Giraffe: Nor me – though I stretched up tall as tall.

Lark: Mole has it, look.

Mole: I do? Oh! Yes, I do!

A pause.

Elephant:	That was just a practice.
Mole:	Ah. Of course.
Wolf:	Right.
Hippo:	Yeah.
Giraffe:	Oh, hoorah! Another chance for me me me!
Elephant:	Watch the gooseberry: up it goes. Who will catch it? No one knows. Except it'll be Us, of course.

As before, Mole cowers while the rest compete. Lark flies up and catches the gooseberry mid-air.

Elephant:	Have We snuffed it up Our trunk? Can someone see it?
Hippo:	It's gone into orbit.
Wolf:	The sun's swallowed it.
Giraffe:	It's stuck to the sky!
Lark:	No, I think Mole has it.
Mole:	I do? Oh! Oh! I do!
Wolf/ Hippo:	Wow! Twice?

Elephant:	Well, that didn't count. The King wasn't ready. We'll try again.
Hippo:	Well, what do you know!
Wolf:	Elephant gets another go.
Giraffe:	'fraid so, Mole.
Mole:	Hey ho.
All:	Okay, then THROW!

Lark: Up it goes – a red globe, a tiny speck.

Hippo: It's melted.

Wolf: Disappeared.

Giraffe: The moon's eaten it.

Lark catches the gooseberry and drops it into Mole's trembling paws.

Mole: Goodness, who'd have thought it.
I seem to have caught it.

Elephant: Best of ten.

Wolf: Since when?

Giraffe: Say again?

Elephant: I set the rules, don't I? I'm King!

Hippo: Not any more, you're not!

Giraffe: Yes. Mole caught it fair and square.

Mole: I think I must have!

Lark: Congratulations, Mole. What do you others say – Zebra, Tiger and Armadillo, Lemur and Silverback Gorillo?

All: WE'RE ALL AGREED!

Mole: I can be King of the Beasts? Really?

Lark: And a very kind and velvety king you'll make.

Mole: I'll certainly try!

Elephant ties his trunk in a knot and stomps off. Offstage, he snorts.

Elephant: Harrumph!

Giraffe: What's that noise, do you suppose?

Wolf: That'll be Elephant blowing his nose.